Professional ethics

Workbook

second edition

Jo Osborne

osborne
BOOKS

Published by Osborne Books Limited
Unit 1B Everoak Estate
Bromyard Road
Worcester WR2 5HP
Tel 01905 748071
Email books@osbornebooks.co.uk
Website www.osbornebooks.co.uk

Design by Laura Ingham
Cover and page design image © Istockphoto.com/Petrovich9

Printed and bound by CPI Group (UK) Ltd, Croydon, CR0 4YY

British Library Cataloguing in Publication Data
A catalogue record for this book is available from the British Library

ISBN 978 1905777 815

Contents

Chapter activities

Chapter activity answers

Practice assessments

Practice assessments – answers

Acknowledgements

The publisher wishes to thank the following for their help with the reading and production of the book: Maz Loton, Jon Moore, Sheriden Amos and Cathy Turner. Thanks are also due to Roger Petheram for his editorial work and to Laura Ingham for her designs for this series.

The publisher is indebted to the Association of Accounting Technicians for its kind permission to reproduce sample practice assessment material.

Author

Jo Osborne is a Chartered Accountant who trained with Ernst & Young in their London office. She then moved to Cable & Wireless where she spent two years in their internal audit department before moving into an investment appraisal role. Jo has taught AAT at Hillingdon College and until recently at Worcester College of Technology where she took on the role of AAT Coordinator.

Introduction

what this book covers

This book has been written specifically to cover the Learning Area 'Professional ethics in accounting and finance' which covers the QCF Unit in the AAT Level 3 Diploma in Accounting: 'Professional ethics in accounting and finance.'

The book may also be used as required by AAT for the Level 2 Certificate in Accounting.

what this book contains

This book is set out in two sections:

Chapter activities which provide extra practice material in addition to the activities included in the Osborne Books Tutorial text. Answers to the Chapter activities are set out in this book.

Practice Assessments are included to prepare the student for the Computer Based Assessments. They are based directly on the structure, style and content of the sample assessment material provided by the AAT at www.aat.org.uk. Suggested answers to the Practice Assessments are set out in this book.

online support from Osborne Books

This book is supported by practice material available at www.osbornebooks.co.uk

This material is available to tutors – and to students at their discretion – in two forms:

A **Tutor Zone** which is available to tutors who have adopted the Osborne Books texts. This area of the website provides extra assessment practice material (plus answers) in addition to the activities included in this Workbook text.

Online learning – online practice questions designed to familiarise students with the style of the AAT Computer Based Assessments.

Scan the code on the right using your Smartphone to gain access to the online practice questions.

further information

If you want to know more about our products, please visit www.osbornebooks.co.uk, email books@osbornebooks.co.uk or telephone Osborne Books Customer Services on 01905 748071.

Chapter activities

1 Chapter activities
Principles of professional ethics

1.1 The document issued by the AAT providing guidance to full and student members regarding professional ethics is called which of the following?

✓

AAT Rules on Professional Ethics	
AAT Principles on Professional Ethics	
AAT Code of Professional Ethics	

1.2 Which one of the following is not an objective of the accounting profession?

✓

Mastering of particular skills and techniques acquired through learning and education and maintained through professional development	
Acknowledgement of duties to society as a whole in addition to the employer or the client	
Rendering personal services to generally accepted standards of conduct and performance	
An outlook which is essentially objective, obtained by being fair minded and free from conflicts of interest	

1.3 Which one of the following is not one of the five Fundamental Principles of Professional Ethics?

✓

Objectivity	
Confidentiality	
Technical competence and due care	
Integrity	

1.4 Complete the following sentence by selecting the appropriate option from the list below:

When a member is faced with a situation that he/she feels may cause a conflict of interest which could affect his/her professional judgement, he/she will have to consider the fundamental principle of ....

- ▨ Integrity
- ▨ Objectivity
- ▨ Professional behaviour

1.5 Charlie works for an accounting practice. One of her clients has asked for some detailed inheritance tax advice. The firm does not have any members of staff with the necessary skills to give this advice. Which of the following fundamental principles could this compromise?

✓

Professional competence and due care	
Objectivity	
Professional behaviour	

1.6   A member of your accounting staff has submitted an expense claim for approval. For one client he has claimed travel expenses for a week when you are certain that he was given a lift in another member of staff's car.

(a)   Should you approve his travel expense claim? | Yes/No |

(b)   Which fundamental principle is being compromised by the member of staff in this situation?

✓

Integrity	
Objectivity	
Professional behaviour	

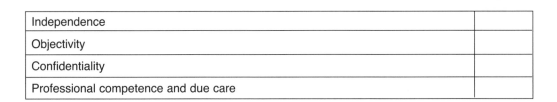

2 Chapter activities
Objectivity and professional competence

2.1 When faced with an ethical dilemma an AAT member should follow a set of rules laid down in the AAT Code of Professional Ethics.

> True/False

2.2 'Any reasonable person who comes into contact with an accountant must be confident that he/she always behaves independently.'

The statement above is an explanation of which of the following?

	✓
Independence of mind	
Independence in appearance	

2.3 Sandra is a partner in an accounting practice. On the Friday before Christmas a case of 12 bottles of champagne is delivered to the accounting practice. The card attached says 'Happy Christmas, see you at the meeting in the New Year!' and was signed by one of the firm's clients.

Which of the following could be affected if Sandra accepts the champagne?

(tick all that could be affected)

	✓
Independence	
Objectivity	
Confidentiality	
Professional competence and due care	

2.4 Arthur believes that a significant ethical conflict has arisen from pressure that has been put on him by his manager at Crumps Ltd who is encouraging him to deliberately include inaccurate figures in the organisation's VAT return to reduce its VAT liability. Which of the following would be sensible steps for Arthur to take?

(tick all that apply)

✓

Seek legal advice	
Contact the police	
Contact the AAT Ethics Advice Line	
Resign from the organisation immediately	
Use the formal dispute process of Crumps Ltd	

2.5 Complete the following sentence by selecting the appropriate words or phrases from the list below.

When a member is faced with an ethical conflict it is important that he/she keeps .... If he/she then has a problem resolving the ethical conflict he/she should contact .... or take ....

- ■ his manager informed
- ■ police
- ■ HMRC
- ■ calm
- ■ the board of directors
- ■ written records
- ■ the AAT ethics advice line
- ■ legal advice

2.6 Which of the following is an objective of the accounting profession?

✓

Mastering of particular skills and techniques acquired through learning and education and maintained through continuing professional development.	
Undertake specific training and education by completing the CPD cycle on a regular basis.	

2.7 How often does the AAT require a member to complete the CPD cycle?

✓

At least once a year	
At least twice a year	
At least three times a year	

2.8 Complete the gaps in the following statement by selecting the appropriate words from the list below.

The AAT CPD policy .... that members in practice undertake sufficient CPD to ensure

their .... to carry out the services that they are .... to provide.

- ▨ recommends
- ▨ licensed
- ▨ competence
- ▨ experience
- ▨ requires
- ▨ advertised

3 Chapter activities
Confidentiality and taxation services

3.1 Complete the gaps in the following statement by selecting the appropriate words or phrases from the list below.

Members of the AAT have an .... to respect the .... of information about a

.... or .... affairs which has been gained during their employment or during

the course of their professional work.

■	client's	■	obligation
■	employer's	■	expectation
■	financial interests	■	confidentiality
■	AAT member's	■	colleague's

3.2 An accountant only has a duty of confidentiality to an employer while he/she is employed by them.

True/False

3.3 From the following list, identify where it is acceptable to disclose confidential information.

(tick all that apply)

	✓
When disclosure is required by law.	
When the information does not relate to the current financial year.	
When authorised by the client or employer.	
When the professional relationship between the accountant and the client has been terminated.	

3.4 Renee has been asked by Jacob, one of her clients, to provide him with some financial information about another of her clients who is a customer of Jacob's and who he believes is in financial difficulty.

Should Renee provide Jacob with any information about the customer? | Yes/No |

3.5 An accountant has a professional duty to disclose confidential information in which of the following circumstances?

(tick all that apply)

	✓
To comply with technical standards and ethical requirements.	
To comply with the requirements of the accountancy practice which employs him/her.	
To comply with the quality review of an IFAC member body or other relevant professional body.	
To protect his/her professional interests in legal proceedings.	

3.6 Enforcement of the requirements of the Data Protection Act is carried out by which of the following?

✓

Information Control Office	
Official Information Controller	
Information Commissioner's Office	

3.7 Which one of the following is <u>not</u> one of the eight principles included in the Data Protection Act that must be complied with when holding personal information?

✓

Fairly and lawfully processed	
Adequate, relevant and not excessive	
Held securely	
Only accessible by qualified staff	

3.8 Leandra is a member who owns and runs her own accounting practice with nine employees. She has failed to tell the Information Commissioner of the way in which the practice processes data about its staff and clients.

Respond to the following statement by ticking the appropriate box.

✓

	True	False
Leandra has committed a criminal offence under the Data Protection Act and consequently could be fined if convicted.		

3.9 What is the name of the process by which the person in an organisation who controls data informs the ICO about the way data is handled?

	✓
Notification	
Registration	
Membership	

3.10 When an accountant carries out tax services for a client, ultimate responsibility for the tax affairs of the client lies with which of the following?

	✓
The client	
The accountant	

4 Chapter activities
Ethics and the employed accountant

4.1

(a) Ahmed is a member of the AAT who works in the accounts department of a large firm of builders. His manager is putting pressure on him to write off a number of customer invoices as the managing director has agreed that these customers can pay cash and avoid paying VAT. Ahmed is aware that this is illegal and is faced with a conflict of loyalties. What is the first step that Ahmed should take in this situation?

	✓
Report the company to HMRC immediately	
Report the company to the AAT	
Try to persuade his employer to change to a legal way of operating	

(b) If the first step that Ahmed takes in (a) above does not work which of the following should Ahmed consider?

	✓
Resigning from his job	
Doing what his manager is asking him to do	

4.2 The Public Interest Disclosure Act 1998 is often referred to as which of the following?

	✓
The Whistleblowers Regulations	
The Whistleblowers Charter	
The Whistleblowers Act	

4.3   Complete the following sentence by selecting the appropriate word from the list below.

An employee will be protected from dismissal provided he/she .... believes that the information disclosed is true.

- ◼   definitely
- ◼   reasonably

4.4   Which of the following disclosures is not specifically covered by the Public Interest Disclosure Act?

✓

Breach of a legal obligation	
Professional misconduct	
Environmental damage	
Miscarriage of justice	

4.5   Jensen is an AAT member employed in the finance department of Rollings Ltd. He has been asked by his manager, Edith, to undertake the lead role for a major review of the finances of a research and development project. Jensen does not have sufficient specific training or experience to carry out this project.

Complete the following sentence by selecting the appropriate option.

Jensen can still carry out the project if ...

✓

he ensures that he tells Edith that he does not have the necessary expertise.	
Edith ensures that he has adequate support when carrying out the project.	

4.6 The Basel Committee Report defines what as follows?

'The risk of loss resulting from inadequate or failed internal processes, people and systems or from external events.'

	✓
Operational risk	
Control risk	
Risk of fraud	

4.7 Stephens & Rowe are the accountants for Toni's Italian Restaurant. The owner, Toni, is putting pressure on Anton, the manager on the assignment, to come in under budget and therefore reduce the fee. Despite Anton explaining that this would not be ethical Toni has offered Anton and his family a free meal and a case of wine.

Which of the following courses of action should Anton follow?

	✓
Take up Toni's offer and attempt to reduce the fees without compromising the quality of the work.	
Raise the issue with one of the partners at Stephens and Rowe.	

4.8 Offering a gift in order to motivate a person to do something is known as which of the following?

	✓
Enticement	
Inducement	
Incentive	

4.9 There has recently been a change of government and the new government intends to raise the rate of corporation tax. What type of operational risk may this present for a profitable business?

	✓
Physical event risk	
Social event risk	
Political event risk	
Economic event risk	

5 Chapter activities
Ethics and the member in practice

5.1   Select which of the following statements is correct.

	✓
An AAT member is permitted to work on an external audit team provided he/she is supervised by a suitably qualified professional accountant.	
An AAT member is permitted to provide external audit services to a client provided he/she has been qualified for at least five years.	

5.2

(a)   Jonas is employed by Samuels & Fox and has been part of an assurance team for its client Rothay plc for the last four years. Jonas has been approached by the Finance Director of Rothay plc with an offer of a senior position in the finance team.

Complete the following sentence by selecting the appropriate option from the list below.

This situation presents a potential .... threat.

■   self-interest

■   familiarity

■   intimidation

(b)   Answer the following question by selecting the appropriate option.

Which TWO of the following safeguards should Samuels & Fox have in place?

	✓
A policy preventing Jonas from entering into employment discussions whilst employed by them.	
A policy requiring Jonas to notify the firm immediately of such an offer.	
A policy requiring Jonas to resign immediately if an offer of employment is received from an assurance client.	
A policy requiring Jonas to be removed from the assurance team for Rothay plc.	

5.3 Select the missing words or phrases from the list below to complete the following sentence.

An intimidation threat to a member's fundamental principles may occur when a ....

exerts .... on a member.

- ■ manager
- ■ undue pressure
- ■ any pressure
- ■ client

5.4 Sanjay is a self-employed accountant for a number of local businesses. He is keen to expand his business and mentions this to one of his clients, James Robbins. James suggests that he invests in Sanjay's business.

This situation presents a potential ....

- ■ finance interest threat.
- ■ intimidation threat.
- ■ self-interest threat.

5.5 There is a potential threat to a member's fundamental principles where the member provides consultancy services to clients. Which of the following will help minimise this threat?

	✓
Make recommendations but do not make management decisions.	
Do not make recommendations but do make management decisions.	
Do not make recommendations or management decisions.	

5.6

(a) Ollie is a member in practice who performs accounting services for Excelsior Ltd and Greenlake Ltd. Excelsior is a supplier to Greenlake. The Finance Director of Excelsior has asked Ollie for his opinion on the financial stability of Greenlake, as he is concerned about the length of time they are taking to pay.

Complete the following sentence by selecting the appropriate option from the list below.

For Ollie this situation threatens the fundamental ethical principles of ...

	✓
objectivity and confidentiality	
Integrity and objectivity	
confidentiality and professional behaviour	

(b) Which of the options below should Ollie take to minimise this threat?

	✓
Give the Finance Director the information that he needs as the fee income he receives from Excelsior is higher than from Greenlake.	
Refuse to provide the information under any circumstances.	
Ask permission from the management of Greenlake before providing the information to the Finance Director of Excelsior.	

5.7 Which of the following is NOT a safeguard against threats to a member's fundamental principles?

	✓
The AAT continuing professional development cycle.	
A policy of refusing to take on an assignment if any potential threat to fundamental principles cannot be sufficiently reduced or removed.	
Regular rotation of senior staff involved in an assurance engagement.	
Ensuring there is no business relationship between an existing client and a potential client before taking on a new client.	

5.8   Ryan, a member in practice, has received £750 commission from an insurance advisor for recommending them to one of his clients. What should Ryan do with this money?

Select the correct option from the list below.

	✓
Send the commission back to the insurance advisor.	
Keep the money but do not tell the client about it.	
Give the money to the client unless the client agrees that Ryan should keep it.	

5.9   Under the terms of what legislation is a member prevented from holding client monies for investment business?

Select the correct answer from the following options.

	✓
Fraud Act 2006	
Proceeds of Crime Act 2002	
Financial Services and Markets Act 2000	

5.10   Review the following definition and decide which of the options below it defines.

'An intentional deception made for personal gain or to damage another individual.'

	✓
Money laundering	
Fraud	

5.11 Georgie, a member of the AAT works as a sole practitioner. She regularly completes a tax return for one of her clients, Yusuke. He has asked her to hold onto the £4,000 that he owes until it is due to HMRC.

Answer the following question by selecting the appropriate option.

What should Georgie do in this situation?   ✓

Draw up a contract with Yusuke before depositing the money in her business bank account.	
Hold Yusuke's money separately from the business's money.	
Deposit the money in a separate account after first deducting her fee for the tax work she has carried out.	

5.12 Marlene is a member in practice. Her client, Phillip, has offered her two tickets for a hit musical which cost him £400.

If Marlene accepts the tickets, which two of her fundamental principles may be threatened?

                                                                                            ✓

Confidentiality and Professional behaviour	
Professional behaviour and Objectivity	
Objectivity and Confidentiality	
Professional competence and due care and Integrity	

6   Chapter activities
Taking on new clients

6.1   Which of the following best describes the primary purpose of a letter of engagement?

	✓
To confirm the fees that the accountant will charge to the client.	
To set out the extent of work to be undertaken by the accountant and the respective responsibilities of the accountant and the client.	

6.2   Which of the following is normally included in a letter of engagement?

(tick all that apply)

	✓
Details of how the accountant's fees will be calculated.	
The client's responsibility to detect errors and fraud.	
The nature and scope of the assignment.	
A detailed schedule of what elements of the assignment each member of the team will be responsible for.	

6.3   An accountant should normally base his/her fees on which of the following factors?

(tick all that apply)

	✓
The skills and knowledge needed for the work involved	
The time that will be needed to carry out the assignment	
The fees that competitors are currently charging for similar assignments	
The level of training and experience needed by the staff	

6.4 When quoting for a new assignment an accountant can simply provide a very low estimate of his/her fees to improve the chances of getting the business, knowing that the fee will increase to the client once the work is started.

True/False

6.5 Complete the following paragraph by selecting the appropriate words or phrases from the list below.

When accepting a new appointment an accountant will send a .... letter to the client's

previous accountant confirming that there are no reasons why he/she should not work for the client.

The existing accountant has a .... to co-operate fully and to provide a

.... answer.

- duty of care
- prompt
- professional responsibility
- professional clearance
- brief
- engagement

6.6   A member must consider Money Laundering Regulations as part of his/her customer due diligence if he/she is going to act for a client in relation to transactions amounting to what sum of money?

✓

10,000 euros	
15,000 euros	
25,000 euros	
Any amount of money, there is no lower limit	

6.7   Francis is an AAT member in practice. He is currently drawing up an advertisement for his accounting practice and is considering including information about the quality of his staff. Which of the following points should he select for inclusion in the advertisement?

✓

Stating in the advertisement that he and the majority of his staff are fully qualified members of the AAT	
Stating that the work of another local accounting practice is of an inferior quality because they employ predominately unqualified staff	

6.8   Henry, an AAT member in practice is considering employing a new member of staff and has interviewed a number of possible candidates. One particularly good candidate has offered to bring her previous employer's client list and to introduce as many as possible to Henry.

In order to behave in an ethical manner what is the appropriate action for Henry to take?

✓

Accept the client list and offer the candidate the job - she has shown good business sense.	
Report her to the AAT for breach of the fundamental principle of confidentiality.	
Do not offer her the job due to her lack of integrity.	
Offer her the job but decline her offer of the client list.	

6.9   Serena Amos is an AAT member who works as a sole practitioner. Which one of the following options is the only appropriate business name that Serena could use for her practice?

	✓
Amos and Associates	
Serena Amos Accountancy Services	
Serena Amos, MAAT	

7 Chapter activities
Legal considerations

7.1

(a) Katrin, a member in practice, has agreed to prepare a Fixed Asset Register for her client, Rhodri. The ownership of the Fixed Asset Register when completed belongs to which of the following?

	✓
Katrin	
Rhodri	

(b) Later in the year Rhodri asks Katrin to complete his tax return and to act as his agent in correspondence with HM Revenue & Customs. Letters sent and received to and from HMRC belong to which of the following?

	✓
Katrin	
Rhodri	

7.2 Which of the following conditions must exist for an AAT member in practice to have a right of lien over a client's documents?

(tick all that apply)

Condition	Right of lien exists
The documents belong to the client.	
The documents are in the member's possession by proper means.	
The documents are in the member's possession by whatever means.	
Work has been carried out by the member on the documents for which the client has paid the fees.	
Work has been carried out by the member on the documents for which the fee remains outstanding.	

7.3   From the list below select the two types of lien.

(tick two options)

	✓
Specific lien	
General lien	
Creditor lien	
Particular lien	

7.4   Select the appropriate words from the list below to complete this definition of liability.

'Having .... responsibility for something with the possibility of having to pay

.........................'

- ▨   damages
- ▨   legal
- ▨   fees
- ▨   professional

7.5   Insurance taken out by an accountant as cover against the legal liability to compensate a client for breach of the accountant's contract of due care is known as which of the following?

	✓
Professional liability insurance	
Professional legal insurance	
Professional indemnity insurance	

7.6 Investing the proceeds of crime into other financial products is only a criminal offence if the amount involved exceeds £200.

True/False

7.7 In addition to the Money Laundering Regulations which two of the following pieces of legislation relate to money laundering.

(tick two options)

	✓
Proceeds of Crime Act 2002	
Fraud Act 2006	
Terrorism Act 2000	

7.8 If an individual is found guilty of money laundering the maximum fine that can be imposed is which of the following?

	✓
10% of the amount involved in the money laundering.	
£50,000	
There is no limit on the fine that can be imposed.	

7.9 The maximum penalty for failing to disclose a suspicion of money laundering is which of the following?

	✓
Two years imprisonment.	
Five years imprisonment.	
There is no maximum limit.	

7.10 Complete the following sentence by selecting the appropriate words or phrases in the list below.

A member who discovers that a .... is potentially money laundering must report his/her

suspicions to the ....or to ....They must ensure that they do not make the

.... aware of this as this would be considered ....

■ client
■ MLRO
■ SOCA
■ tipping off
■ failure to disclose
■ client

7.11 An AAT member who forms a suspicion of money laundering when he is attending a social occasion with one of his clients has a duty to report this suspicion.

True/False

8 Chapter activities

Regulations of the accounting profession

8.1 The AAT Code of Professional Ethics is an example of criminal law.

True/False

8.2 Which of the following are operating bodies within the Financial Reporting Council?

(tick all appropriate options)

	✓
Accounting Standards Board	
Financial Reporting Review Panel	
International Federation of Accountants	
Professional Oversight Board	

8.3 The following is a definition of which of the options below?

'An independent person or organisation whose task it is to police a particular industry, ensuring that member companies do not act illegally.'

	✓
Ombudsman	
Watchdog	

8.4

(a) A code of business ethics in an organisation is not legally enforceable.

> True/False

(b) Complete the following sentence by selecting the appropriate option.

In addition to helping an individual make the right choice in an ethical dilemma business ethics are designed to help ensure ....

	✓
individuals know to whom in the organisation they should refer an ethical problem.	
there is a consistency in the ethical behaviour of all employees in an organisation.	

8.5 Identify which of the following business values are among those set out in the Nolan Principles.

	✓
Selflessness	
Integrity	
Management	
Honesty	
Accountability	

8.6 Ralph, a member of the AAT, has not complied with the AAT Code of Professional Ethics. Complete the following sentence by selecting the appropriate option from the choices below.

The AAT will take disciplinary action against Ralph...

	✓
if his employer notifies the AAT of his non-compliance	
immediately	
if his conduct reflects adversely on the reputation of the AAT	

8.7 Identify which of the following professional accounting bodies is a sponsoring body of the AAT

(tick all that apply)

	✓
ICAI	
IFAC	
ICAEW	
CIMA	
ACCA	
CIPFA	
ICAS	

8.8 The CCAB provides a forum where matters affecting the accounting professional as a whole can be discussed so that the profession can speak with one voice.

CCAB stands for which of the following?

	✓
Chartered Committee of Accounting Bodies	
Consultative Committee of Accounting Bodies	
Certified Committee of Accounting Bodies	

8.9 The three elements of the Institute of Business Ethics simple ethical test are what?

(tick three options)

	✓
Transparency	
Integrity	
Objectivity	
Effect	
Fairness	
Legality	

Answers to chapter activities

1 Chapter activities
Principles of professional ethics

1.1 AAT Code of Professional Ethics

1.2 Rendering personal services to generally accepted standards of conduct and performance

1.3 Technical competence and due care

1.4 When a member is faced with a situation that he/she feels may cause a conflict of interest which could affect his/her professional judgement he/she will have to consider the fundamental principle of **objectivity**.

1.5 Professional competence and due care

1.6 (a) No

(b) Integrity

2 Chapter activities
Objectivity and professional competence

2.1 False

2.2 Independence in appearance

2.3 Independence

Objectivity

2.4 Seek legal advice

Contact the AAT ethics advice line

Use the formal dispute process of the organisation who employs him/her (Crumps Ltd).

2.5 When a member is faced with an ethical conflict it is important that he/she keeps **written records**. If he/she then has a problem resolving the ethical conflict he/she should contact the **AAT ethics advice line** or take **legal advice**.

2.6 Mastering of particular skills and techniques acquired through learning and education and maintained through continuing professional development.

2.7 At least twice a year.

2.8 The AAT CPD policy **requires** that members in practice undertake sufficient CPD to ensure their **competence** to carry out the services that they are **licensed** to provide.

3 Chapter activities
Confidentiality and taxation services

3.1 Members of the AAT have an **obligation** to respect the **confidentiality** of information about a **client's** or **employer's** affairs which has been gained during their employment or during the course of their professional work.

3.2 False

3.3 The following apply:

When disclosure is required by law

When authorised by the client or employer

3.4 No

3.5 The following apply:

To comply with technical standards and ethical requirements

To comply with the quality review of an IFAC member body or other relevant professional body

To protect his/her professional interests in legal proceedings.

3.6 Information Commissioner's Office

3.7 Only accessible by qualified staff.

3.8 True

3.9 Notification

3.10 The client

4 Chapter activities
Ethics and the employed accountant

4.1 (a) Try to persuade his employer to change to a legal way of operating.

   (b) Resigning from his job.

4.2 The Whistleblowers Charter

4.3 An employee will be protected from dismissal provided he/she **reasonably** believes that the information disclosed is true.

4.4 Professional misconduct

4.5 Jensen can still carry out the project **if Edith ensures that he has adequate support when carrying out the project.**

4.6 Operational risk

4.7 Raise the issue with one of the partners at Stephens and Rowe.

4.8 Inducement

4.9 Political event risk

5 Chapter activities
Ethics and the member in practice

5.1 An AAT member is permitted to work on an external audit team provided he/she is supervised by a suitably qualified professional accountant.

5.2 (a) This situation presents a potential **self-interest** threat.

(b) A policy requiring Jonas to notify the firm immediately of such an offer.

A policy requiring Jonas to be removed from the assurance team for Rothay plc.

5.3 An intimidation threat to a member's fundamental principles may occur when a **client** exerts **undue pressure** on a member.

5.4 This situation presents a potential **finance interest threat**.

5.5 Make recommendations but do not make management decisions.

5.6 (a) Objectivity and confidentiality.

(b) Ask permission from the management of Greenlake before providing the information to the Finance Director of Excelsior.

5.7 Ensuring there is no business relationship between an existing client and a potential client before taking on a new client.

5.8 Give the money to the client unless the client agrees that Ryan should keep it.

5.9 Financial Services and Markets Act 2000

5.10 Fraud

5.11 Hold Yusuke's money separately from the business's money.

5.12 Professional behaviour and Objectivity

6 Chapter activities
Taking on new clients

6.1 To set out the extent of work to be undertaken by the accountant and the respective responsibilities of the accountant and the client.

6.2 The following apply:

Details of how the accountant's fees will be calculated

The client's responsibility to detect errors and fraud

The nature and scope of the assignment

6.3 The following apply:

The skills and knowledge needed for the work involved

The time that will be needed to carry out the assignment

The level of training and experience needed by the staff

6.4 False

6.5 When accepting a new appointment an accountant will send a **professional clearance** letter to the client's previous accountant confirming that there are no reasons why he/she should not work for the client. The existing accountant has a **professional responsibility** to co-operate fully and to provide a **prompt** answer.

6.6 15,000 euros.

6.7 Stating in the advertisement that he and the majority of his staff are fully qualified members of the AAT.

6.8 Do not offer her the job due to her lack of integrity

6.9 Serena Amos Accountancy Services

7 Chapter activities
Legal considerations

7.1 **(a)** Rhodri

(b) Rhodri

7.2

Condition	Right of lien exists
The documents belong to the client.	✓
The documents are in the member's possession by proper means.	✓
The documents are in the member's possession by whatever means.	
Work has been carried out by the member on the documents for which the client has paid the fees.	
Work has been carried out by the member on the documents for which the fee remains outstanding.	✓

7.3

Specific lien	
General lien	✓
Creditor lien	
Particular lien	✓

7.4 'Having **legal** responsibility for something with the possibility of having to pay **damages**.'

7.5 Professional indemnity insurance

7.6 False

7.7

Proceeds of Crime Act 2002	✓
Fraud Act 2006	
Terrorism Act 2000	✓

7.8   There is no limit on the fine that can be imposed.

7.9   Five years imprisonment.

7.10   A member who discovers that a **client** is potentially money laundering must report his/her suspicions to the **MLRO** or to **SOCA**. They must ensure that they do not make the client aware of this as this would be considered **tipping off.**

7.11   False

8 Chapter activities
Regulations of the accounting profession

8.1   False

8.2

Accounting Standards Board	✓
Financial Reporting Review Panel	✓
International Federation of Accountants	
Professional Oversight Board	✓

8.3   Watchdog

8.4   **(a)**   True

(b)   In addition to helping an individual make the right choice in an ethical dilemma business ethics are designed to help ensure **there is a consistency in the ethical behaviour of all employees in an organisation.**

8.5

Selflessness	✓
Integrity	✓
Management	
Honesty	✓
Accountability	✓

8.6   The AAT will take disciplinary action against Ralph **if his conduct reflects adversely on the reputation of the AAT.**

8.7   The following apply:

ICAEW, CIMA, CIPFA, ICAS

8.8   Consultative Committee of Accounting Bodies

8.9

Transparency	✓
Integrity	
Objectivity	
Effect	✓
Fairness	✓
Legality	

Professional ethics

Practice assessment 1

Section 1

Task 1.1

Complete the following sentences by selecting the appropriate option from each list below.

(a) 'A member must not let his/her own bias or pressure from others affect decisions that he/she makes. This is following the fundamental principle of …

■ objectivity.'

■ professional behaviour.'

■ confidentiality.'

(b) 'The conceptual framework approach requires members to …

■ take ethical decisions that comply with the fundamental ethical principles.'

■ comply with a set of specific rules set out in the AAT Code of Professional Ethics.'

Task 1.2

Answer the following questions by selecting the appropriate option in each case.

(a)   Which of the following are objectives of the accounting profession?

✓

Mastering of particular skills and techniques acquired through learning and education and maintained through continuing professional development.	
Acknowledgement of duties to the accounting profession as a whole in addition to the employer or the client.	
Rendering personal services to acceptable standards of conduct and performance.	

(b)   In the UK, the Financial Reporting Council has direct responsibility for which of the following?

✓

Enforcing disciplinary procedures against any members of all the professional accounting bodies.	
Providing a forum to enable the accounting profession to speak with one voice on important matters.	
Overseeing the regulatory activities of all the professional accounting bodies.	

(c)   An ombudsman is appointed by the government.

True/False

Task 1.3

Identify whether each of the following professional accountancy bodies listed below are, or are not, members of the Consultative Committee of Accounting Bodies (CCAB).

Is a member of CCAB	Is not a member of CCAB

- ◼ ICAEW
- ◼ FRC
- ◼ CIPFA

- ◼ ICAS
- ◼ ACCA
- ◼ AAT

- ◼ IFAC
- ◼ ICAI
- ◼ CIMA

Task 1.4

(a) Respond to the following statement by selecting the appropriate option.

✓

	True	False
The AAT Code of Professional Ethics is an example of criminal law.		

(b) Complete the following sentence by selecting the appropriate words from the list below.

It is .... for a business to introduce an ethical code, but it is not ....

- ◼ a legal requirement
- ◼ advisable

Task 1.5

(a)   Complete the following sentence by selecting the appropriate option from the list below.

According to the .... Committee on Banking Supervision, the definition of

.... risk is the risk of loss resulting from inadequate or failed internal

....................., people and systems or from external events.

■	control	■	processes	■	Nolan
■	management	■	Basel	■	operational

(b)   Edina, a member in practice, has been approached by Fernando, the proprietor of a local retail business, who wishes to enter into a long-term professional relationship with Edina's practice.

Answer the following question by selecting the appropriate option.

As part of her customer due diligence processes, which of the following actions must Edina take?

	✓
Verify with HMRC that the business is registered for VAT and PAYE.	
Verify the client has the financial means to pay her fees.	
Verify the client's identity on the basis of documents, data or other reliable information.	

Task 1.6

(a) Place the four stages of the AAT CPD cycle shown below in the order that they should be carried out.

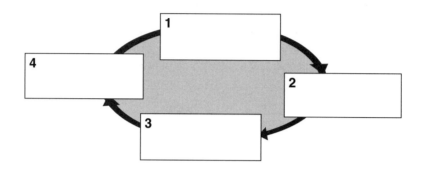

■ Action

■ Plan

■ Assess

■ Evaluate

(b) Carrying out the CPD cycle is a requirement from the AAT for its members.

True/False

Task 1.7

(a)　Jake is a partner in a small firm of accountants which has recently taken on Alice, who is AAT part-qualified. Alice explains that she is still in touch with some of her old colleagues at the firm she trained with and would have no problems getting details of the firm's current clients and the accounting fees that they pay. She can also find out from her friends which clients are not happy with the service they are getting from her former employer.

Answer the following question by selecting the appropriate option.

In order to behave in an ethical manner in these circumstances, what is the most appropriate action for Jake to take?

	✓
Sack Alice immediately.	
Take Alice's offer; after all, if the clients are unhappy with their existing accountants they will get a better service with Jake's firm.	
Explain to Alice that it would be unethical to agree to her offer as they would both be breaching the fundamental principles of integrity and confidentiality.	

(b)　Freddie, an AAT member in practice, has been accused of bringing the profession into disrepute when advertising his professional services.

Complete the following sentence by selecting the appropriate option from the list below.

'This accusation is most likely to arise if Freddie . . .

	✓
says in his marketing material that he is a more ethical accountant than any other accountancy firm in the area.'	
refers to the fact that all his staff are either AAT qualified or studying for the qualification.'	
states that his staff are prepared to travel to any location in the country.'	

(c)　Lily Robinson is an AAT member who has recently been promoted to partner in Croft & Wynne LLP, a practice that has branches in England, Scotland, France and Germany. Lily has suggested to the other two partners, Eileen and Jessica, that they change the practice's name to Croft, Wynne & Robinson MAAT International LLP.

Identify the one element of the proposed name that is prohibited by the AAT Code of Professional Ethics, by selecting it from the list below.

Permitted name				Prohibited element
Croft, Wynne & Robinson	LLP	International	MAAT	

(d) Complete the following statement of how members should apply safeguards against threats to their fundamental principles by selecting the appropriate word(s) from the list below.

'In exercising .... a member should consider what a .... and informed third party having knowledge of all relevant information, including the significance of the threat and the safeguards applied, would conclude to be ....

- ■ technical competence
- ■ acceptable
- ■ unacceptable

- ■ reasonable
- ■ professional judgement
- ■ qualified

Task 1.8

(a) Verity, a member in practice, has been approached by Armitage Ltd, a large firm of builders, asking her to carry out some VAT work for them. One of Verity's existing clients, Buildshop, is a local builders merchant. During the course of her work for Buildshop, Verity is aware that that Armitage are disputing two large invoices from Buildshop.

Complete the following sentence by selecting the appropriate option from the list below.

'For Verity this situation threatens both the fundamental principles of . . .

- ■   objectivity and confidentiality.'

- ■   confidentiality and professional competence.'

- ■   objectivity and professional behaviour.'

(b) Jim is an AAT member in business, working for a firm of surveyors. His sister, Rosie, is considering an offer of a senior post with a local property development company. If Rosie accepts the post it would mean that she would be in a position to influence whether Jim's company was contracted by her employer.

Answer the following question by selecting the appropriate option.

What should Jim do in this situation?

Resign from his position with the surveyors.	
Advise Rosie of relevant threats and safeguards that will protect him should his employer enter into any future contracts with Rosie's organisation.	
Immediately inform higher levels of management.	

(c) Complete the following sentence by selecting the appropriate option from the list below.

'The requirement for an AAT member in practice to be independent of a client applies in relation to …

- ■   all clients.'

- ■   assurance clients only.'

(d) Harjit is an AAT member in practice with a large local practice, Downton & Price LLP. He has just been selected as part of the team working on new assurance assignment for Silver plc. His wife has a 2% shareholding in Silver plc.

Complete the following sentence by selecting the appropriate option from each list below.

'This situation presents . . .

■   an intimidation threat

■   a self-interest threat

and the best course of action would be . . .

■   to remove Harjit from the assurance engagement.'

■   to make Harjit's wife sell her shares in Silver immediately.'

(e) Roger was employed in the Accounts department of Weavers plc for a number of years. He has recently moved to work for an accountancy practice, Renaissance LLP, who are carrying out an assurance assignment for Weavers plc.

If Roger works on the assurance assignment for Weavers this situation may present ...

■   an intimidation threat

■   a self-interest threat

■   a self-review threat

Choose **one** option.

Answer the following question by selecting the appropriate option.

Which of the following safeguards should Renaissance LLP have in place?

	✓
A policy preventing Renaissance from employing staff who have previously worked for clients.	
A policy preventing Roger from working as part of the assurance team for Weaver plc.	
A policy allowing Roger to work on the assurance team for Weaver plc provided he is not the manager.	

Section 2

Task 2.1

(a)   From the list below identify which business values are included in those set out in the Nolan Principles. Insert them in the table below.

Nolan Principles

Business values		
■ Trust	■	Selflessness
■ Openness	■	Management

(b)   Miles, an AAT member, has provided investment advice to one of his firm's clients. He is not authorised to do this.

Complete the following sentence by selecting the appropriate option from the list below.

'AAT Disciplinary action will be taken against Miles . . .

■   if the client loses money on the investment.'

■   if the authorities find out that he was not authorised to do so.'

■   if his conduct reflects adversely on the reputation of the AAT.'

Task 2.2

(a)   Sam, an AAT member, has a client Roland, who is currently taking legal action against one of his customers. Roland has asked Sam to hold on to £3,000 cash for the next two months in case he loses the case and needs to pay his customer's legal fees.

Answer the following question by selecting the appropriate option.

What should Sam do in this situation?

✓

Agree to hold the money, deposit it in his business account and provide Roland with a receipt.	
Inform Roland that as a member of the AAT he is not permitted to hold client assets.	
Agree to hold the money and open a client account for Roland that is separate from his business account.	

(b)   One of the three classes of fraud defined in the Fraud Act 2006 is 'fraud by failing to disclose information'.

Complete the following definition of this class of fraud by selecting the appropriate words from the list below.

'Where a person fails to disclose .... information to a third party which he/she has

a .... duty to disclose.'

- professional
- any
- legal
- confidential

Task 2.3

(a)   Andrea is an AAT member in practice employed by Shine LLP. She has been working on an assurance engagement for Glimmer Ltd. During the work that she carried out on Glimmer's payroll department Andrea has found out confidential information about the salaries paid to the directors of Glimmer.

Which of the following statements are true?

(tick all that apply)

✓

	True	*False*
Andrea should not disclose this information to any other member of staff at Shine LLP.		
Andrea should not discuss this information with other members of staff at Glimmer Ltd.		
Andrea should not use this information to the advantage of Shine LLP.		
Andrea should not discuss this information with her husband.		

(b)   Suzanne, an AAT member, owns and runs a small accountancy practice with three employees.

Respond to the following statement by selecting the appropriate 'true/false' option:

Suzanne does not need to notify the Information Commissioner of the practice's data processing operations as there are only four members of staff in her business.

True/False

Task 2.4

It is acceptable for AAT members to disclose confidential information in which of the following circumstances?

(tick all that apply)

	✓
Where the information is required as evidence in a court of law.	
When authorised by a client or employer.	
Where the law has been broken and the information has to be disclosed to the relevant authorities.	
When the professional relationship between the client and the member has been terminated.	

Task 2.5

(a) Respond to the following statement by selecting the appropriate 'true/false' option.

Provided a member attaches a disclaimer of professional liability to work that he/she carries out for a client, this will protect the member from legal action by the client for professional negligence.

> True/False

(b) Henrico, an AAT member in practice, has been asked by his employer Hexagon LLP, to manage an assignment from a large new client which includes a significant amount of corporate taxation work. Although Henrico studied tax as part of his AAT qualification, he has not done any further tax work since.

Complete the following sentence by selecting the appropriate option from the list below.

'Henrico may nonetheless undertake the project if he ...

- ensures that a disclaimer of professional liability is attached to the work that he carries out and that the business has adequate professional indemnity insurance.'

- has adequate support.'

- informs the partners at Hexagon that his performance will be lacking in expertise.'

Task 2.6

(a)   Complete the following sentence.

'If a client asks for a document to be produced by an AAT member as part of an assignment then the document will belong to …

■   the client.'

■   the member.'

(b)   Sonya is a member in practice. The firm that she works for has outgrown the premises it currently occupies and is moving to larger offices. One of the partners has asked her to clear out some of the old files that they have stored in the basement. She is unsure which documents she should keep in case they are needed and which should be disposed of.

Complete the following sentence.

'The Limitation Act 1980 states that the time limit for legal actions under simple contract law

is …………………. years.'

Task 2.7

(a) Ellery is an AAT member who works as a sole practitioner. One of his clients, a second-hand car dealership, receives a large amount of cash. Despite Ellery's advice the client refuses to carry out the necessary checks regarding the source of this cash.

Complete the following sentence by selecting the appropriate option from the list below.

'Ellery is obliged to report the client's refusal and the facts surrounding it to ...

- ◼ HM Revenue and Customs (HMRC).'

- ◼ the Serious Organised Crime Agency (SOCA).'

- ◼ the AAT.'

- ◼ the police.'

(b) AAT members only need to report suspicions of a money laundering offence if the amount involved exceeds which of the following?

	✓
£200	
£500	
£1,000	
There is no lower limit	

Task 2.8

Royston, an AAT member employed by Orinoco plc, is facing significant pressure from his employer to intentionally overstate the profits for the year. The Finance Director has suggested that if he does as he is asked he will receive a significantly improved bonus at the end of the year.

Complete the following sentence by selecting the appropriate option from each of the lists.

'Royston is being offered...

■   an inducement

■   an incentive

which will threaten his adherence to the fundamental principles. His immediate response should be to ...

■   overstate the profit for the year as he has been told to do.'

■   obtain advice from the AAT.'

■   resign from Orinoco plc.'

Task 2.9

(a) Amir is an AAT member who is currently part of an assurance team working on a manufacturing client. Amir believes that the client is failing to declare goods imported from abroad and therefore not paying the necessary import duties.

Complete the following sentences by selecting the appropriate option from the list below.

'If Amir does not report his concerns he may be charged with…

■ whistleblowing.'

■ money laundering.'

■ failure to disclose.'

■ tipping off.'

(b) 'However his concerns should not be raised with the client or he may be guilty of…

■ money laundering.'

■ failure to disclose.'

■ tipping off.'

Task 2.10

(a)   The Public Interest Disclosure Act 1998 is sometimes referred to as which of the following?

	✓
The Whistleblowers Charter	
The Money Laundering Regulations	
The Data Protection Act	

(b)   Answer the following question by selecting the appropriate options.

(tick all that apply)

To which of the following disclosures does the Public Interest Disclosure Act 1998 not extend?

	✓
Breach of contract	
Professional negligence	
Environmental damage	
Endangerment of an individual's health and safety	

(c)   Complete the following sentence by selecting the appropriate words from the list below.

'Accounting practices should have training and procedures in place to ensure that they comply with the reporting required for money laundering. If procedures are not in place they may be liable for…

■   a fine and/or imprisonment.'

■   disciplinary procedures.'

■   a professional negligence claim against them.'

Professional ethics

Practice assessment 2

This Assessment is based on a sample assessment provided by the AAT and is reproduced here with their kind permission.

Section 1

Task 1.1

Complete the following sentences by selecting the appropriate option from each list below.

(a) 'The behaviour of a member who is straightforward and honest in all professional and business relationships is following the fundamental principle of …

■ Objectivity.'

■ Professional competence and due care.'

■ Integrity.'

(b) 'The conceptual framework approach requires members to…

■ Comply with a set of specific rules.'

■ Identify, evaluate and respond to threats to compliance with the fundamental principles.'

Task 1.2

Answer the following questions by selecting the appropriate option in each case.

(a)   The accountancy profession is committed to which of the following objectives?

	✓
An outlook, which is essentially commercial, achieved by being business minded and free from regulatory pressure.	
Rendering services to acceptable standards of conduct and performance.	
Acknowledgement of duties to society as a whole in addition to duties to the employer or client.	

(b)   In the UK, which part of the Financial Reporting Council has direct responsibility for reviewing the way in which the professional accountancy bodies regulate their members?

	✓
The Accounting Standards Board (ASB)	
The Accountancy and Actuarial Discipline Board (AADB)	
The Professional Oversight Board (POB)	

(c)   Complete the following sentence by selecting the appropriate option from the list below.

'A code of business ethics in an organisation should be designed to help an individual in the organisation …

- ◾   make the right choice between alternative courses of action.'

- ◾   identify the appropriate person to whom an ethical dilemma should be referred.'

Task 1.3

Identify whether each of the following professional accountancy bodies is or is not a sponsoring body of the AAT by selecting from the list below.

Sponsoring body of the AAT	Not a sponsoring body of the AAT

- ICAI
- ICAEW
- ICAS
- FRC
- IFAC
- CIMA
- CIPFA
- ACCA

Task 1.4

(a)   Respond to the following statement by selecting the appropriate option.

✓

	True	False
The AAT Code of Professional Ethics is an example of civil law.		

(b)   Answer the following question by selecting the appropriate option.

Which of the following is a valid reason for an organisation to introduce an ethical code?

✓

To ensure that there is consistency of conduct by employees across the organisation.	
To impose criminal sanctions on employees who fail to comply with the ethical code.	

Task 1.5

(a)   Complete the following sentence by selecting the appropriate option from the list below.

According to the Basel Committee on Banking Supervision, the definition of operational risk is:

'The risk of direct or indirect loss resulting from inadequate or failed…

■   processes, people and systems.'

■   regulation.'

(b)   Cecily, a member in practice, wishes to enter into a professional relationship with a client which will almost certainly last for at least two years.

Answer the following question by selecting the appropriate option.

As part of her customer due diligence processes, which of the following actions must Cecily take?

	✓
Notify the AAT of the relationship.	
Verify the nature and value of the client's assets.	
Verify the client's identity on the basis of documents, data or other reliable information.	

Task 1.6

(a)   Complete the following sentence by selecting the most appropriate option from the list below.

A member's continuing duty to maintain professional knowledge and skill so that a client or employer receives competent professional service forms part of the fundamental principle of …

■   Integrity.

■   professional competence and due care.

■   professional behaviour.

(b)   Respond to the following statement by selecting the appropriate option.

	✓	
	True	*False*
Within the conceptual framework of threats and safeguards, continuing professional development (CPD) requirements form one of the safeguards created by the profession.		

Task 1.7

(a)   Jacob, an AAT member in practice, is conducting a second interview of an excellent candidate (also an AAT member) for a senior post in Jacob's firm. When discussing remuneration the potential employee states she will bring a copy of the database of clients from her old firm to introduce new clients to Jacob's firm. She also says she knows a lot of negative information about her old firm which Jacob could use to gain clients from them.

Answer the following question by selecting the appropriate option.

In order to behave in an ethical manner in these circumstances, what is the most appropriate action for Jacob to take following the interview?

	✓
Because she shows business acumen, offer her the job.	
Because she has breached the fundamental principles of integrity and confidentiality, report her to the AAT.	
Because she lacks integrity, inform her that she will not be offered the job.	

(b)   Frankie, an AAT member in practice, has been accused of bringing the profession into disrepute when marketing his professional services.

Complete the following sentence by selecting the appropriate option from the list below.

'This accusation is most likely to arise if Frankie…

	✓
states in an advertisement that he is a fully qualified member of the AAT.'	
makes a disparaging reference in an advertisement to the work of Iqbal, an ACCA member.'	
refers in an advertisement to the fact that some if his employees are only part-qualified.'	

(c)   Jessica Murray is an AAT member who has worked for many years in Salim & Wright LLP, a practice that has branches in the UK, Europe and North Africa. She has now become a partner in the practice along with Tim Salim and Godfrey Wright, and Jessica wishes to change the practice's name to Salim, Wright & Murray MAAT International LLP.

Identify the element of the proposed name that is prohibited by the AAT Code of Professional Ethics, by selecting it from the list below.

Permitted name				Prohibited element
Salim, Wright & Murray	MAAT	International	LLP	

(d) Complete the following statement of how a member should apply safeguards against threats in any particular circumstance by selecting the appropriate word(s) from the list below.

'In exercising professional judgement, a member should consider what a reasonable and

informed . . . . .having knowledge of all relevant information, including

the . . . . .of the threat and the safeguards applied, would conclude to

be . . . .

▓ third party	▓ fellow professional	▓ cost
▓ significance	▓ acceptable	▓ Unacceptable

Task 1.8

(a) Vernon, a member in practice, performs book-keeping services for both Yen Ltd and Piston Ltd. The two companies are in dispute about a series of purchases that Yen Ltd made from Piston Ltd.

Complete the following sentence by selecting the appropriate option from the list below.

'For Vernon this situation threatens both the fundamental principles of …

▓   objectivity and confidentiality.'

▓   integrity and professional behaviour.'

▓   confidentiality and professional competence.'

(b) Niall is a member in business. His cousin Oonagh has recently been employed by an organisation with which Niall has regular business dealings. Oonagh's position means that she would be able to offer Niall preferential treatment in the awarding of major contracts.

Answer the following question by selecting the appropriate option.

What should Niall do?

	✓
Seek legal advice.	
Advise Oonagh of relevant threats and safeguards that will protect Niall should he receive such an offer from Oonagh's organisation.	
Immediately inform higher levels of management.	

(c) Complete the following sentence by selecting the appropriate option from the list below.

'The requirement for an AAT member in practice to be independent of a client applies in relation to ...

■ all clients.'

■ assurance clients only.'

(d) Quentin is an AAT member in practice with Topping LLP. He is engaged on an assurance assignment for Nickel plc when he receives news that his grandmother has left him a 1% shareholding in Nickel plc in her will.

Complete the following sentence by selecting the appropriate option from each list below.

'This situation presents a ...

■ familiarity threat.'

■ self-interest threat.'

and the best course of action would be ...

■ to remove Quentin from the assurance engagement.'

■ to inform the audit committee of Nickel plc.'

(e) Helena is employed by Elaprop LLP and has been part of an assurance team for its client, Bowen plc, for three years. Helena has been approached by Bowen plc with an offer of a senior job in the company's finance team.

Complete the following sentence by selecting the appropriate option from the list below.

'This situation presents ...

■ an intimidation threat.'

■ a self-interest threat.'

Answer the following question by selecting the appropriate option.

Which TWO of the following safeguards should Elaprop LLP have in place? ✓

A policy requiring Helena to notify the firm of such an offer.	
A policy preventing Helena from entering employment negotiations with an assurance client.	
A policy requiring Helena to resign from the firm once an offer of employment is received from an assurance client.	
A policy requiring Helena's removal from the assurance engagement with Bowen plc.	

Section 2

Task 2.1

(a)   From the list below identify which business values are included in those set out in the Nolan Principles. Insert them in the table below.

Nolan Principles

Business values		
■ Trust	■	Accountability
■ Transparency	■	Honesty

(b)   Trevor, an AAT member, has not complied with the AAT Code of Professional Ethics.

Complete the following sentence by selecting the appropriate option from the list below.

'Disciplinary action will be taken against Trevor …

■   immediately.'

■   if his employer notifies the AAT of his non-compliance.'

■   if his conduct reflects adversely on the reputation of the AAT.'

Task 2.2

(a)   Gregory, an AAT member, has just started his own accounting business. One of his first clients, Cassandra, has asked Gregory to keep custody of £200 in cash for one month, when it will need to be paid to HM Revenue and Customs in settlement of Cassandra's income tax liability.

Answer the following question by selecting the appropriate option.

What should Gregory do?

✓

Keep a note of the amount of money but hold it in his established bank account.	
Hold the money separately from his own money and that of his business.	
Inform Cassandra that he cannot hold the money as he is not regulated by the Financial Services Authority (FSA).	

(b)   William is an AAT member in practice who acts on behalf of an elderly client, Jordan. Last month William issued an invoice for £5,000 to Jordan for 'safeguarding services', which just involved being sole signatory on Jordan's bank account for a period of one month. He has now transferred £7,000 to himself from Jordan's bank account, in settlement of the invoice plus £2,000 'late fees'. Following a complaint from Jordan's son, the police are now investigating William for fraud.

Answer the following question by selecting the appropriate option.

Which Fraud Act 2006 offence is it most likely that William has committed?

✓

Fraud by false representation.	
Fraud by abuse of position.	
Fraud by failing to disclose information.	

Task 2.3

(a) Alessandro is an AAT member in practice employed by Sueka LLP, He has acquired some information about Polina Ltd in the course of acting for the company on an assurance engagement.

Complete the following sentence by selecting the appropriate option from the list below.

'The principle of confidentiality imposes an obligation on Alessandro to refrain from …

■ using the information to the advantage of Sueka LLP.'

■ disclosing the information within Sueka LLP.'

■ disclosing the information to anyone at all.'

(b) Susan, an AAT member, owns and runs a small accountancy practice with seven employees. She has failed to notify the Information Commissioner of the practice's data processing operations.

Respond to the following statement by selecting the appropriate option.

✓

	True	False
Susan has committed a criminal offence and may be fined if convicted.		

Task 2.4

(a) Answer the following question by selecting the appropriate option.

In which circumstance are AAT members specifically advised to seek professional advice before disclosing confidential information?

	✓
Where there is a professional duty to disclose in the public interest, and this is not prohibited by law.	
Where disclosure is required by law.	
Where disclosure is permitted by law and is authorised by the client or employer.	

(b) Bill is an AAT member in practice as a sole practitioner. He suspects terrorist financing activities are taking place at his client, Hover Ltd.

Complete the following sentence by selecting the appropriate option from the list below.

'Bill should disclose his suspicions concerning Hover Ltd to …

■   the police.'

■   the board of Hover Ltd.'

■   the Serious Organised Crime Agency.'

Task 2.5

   (a)   Complete the following sentence by selecting the appropriate option from the list below.

        'Breach by a member in practice of the duty to exercise reasonable care and skill means the member may be liable to the client for…

- breach of contract and professional negligence.'
- fraud and professional negligence.'
- fraud and breach of confidentiality.'
- breach of contract and breach of confidentiality.'

   (b)   Lionel, an AAT member in business, has been asked by his employer to undertake a major project for which Lionel currently does not have sufficient specific training or experience.

        Complete the following sentence by selecting the appropriate option from the list below.

        'Lionel may nonetheless undertake the project if he …

- has adequate support.'
- informs the employer that his performance will be lacking in expertise.'

Task 2.6

(a)   Patrick is a member in practice in the UK who acts as a principal in relation to his client, Pippa Ltd. To help Pippa Ltd's finance director in his preparation of the company's financial statements, Patrick has agreed to prepare a sales ledger control account reconciliation.

Complete the following sentence by selecting the appropriate option from the list below.

'Ownership of the reconciliation when it is complete is…

■   Patrick's.'

■   Pippa Ltd's.'

(b)   Identify the **three** conditions that must exist for an AAT member in practice to have a right of lien over the documents of a sole trader client, by selecting the relevant conditions from the list below.

✓

Conditions	Right of lien exists
The documents belong to the client.	
The documents belong to a third party.	
The documents are in the member's possession by proper means.	
The documents are in the member's possession, however this has come about.	
Work has been done by the member on the documents for which the fee has been paid.	
Work has been done by the member on the documents for which the fee is outstanding.	

Task 2.7

(a)   Zoe, an AAT member in practice in the UK, works for a large firm of accountants. Zoe has a client which refuses to make disclosure of a known error in its taxation affairs, after having had notice of the error and a reasonable time to reflect.

Complete the following sentence by selecting the appropriate option from the list below.

'Zoe is obliged to report the client's refusal and the facts surrounding it to...

■   HM Revenue and Customs (HMRC).'

■   the Serious Organised Crime Agency (SOCA).'

■   the Money Laundering Reporting Officer (MLRO).'

(b)   Respond to the following statement by selecting the appropriate option.

	True	False
An act of attempting to conceal criminal property is only reportable as a money laundering offence if it involves amounts of £500 or more.		

(c)   Complete the following sentence by inserting the appropriate figure.

'The maximum period of imprisonment that can be imposed on a person found guilty of money laundering is . . . . years.'

Task 2.8

Malcolm, an AAT member employed by Dreed plc, is facing significant pressure from his employer to intentionally mislead the company's internal auditors.

Complete the following sentence by selecting the appropriate option from each dropdown menu.

'Malcolm's situation represents...

■   an intimidation threat

■   a self-review threat

and his immediate response should be to implement the safeguard of...

■   obtaining advice from the AAT.'

■   resigning from Dreed plc.'

Task 2.9

(a)   Complete the following sentence by selecting the appropriate option from the list below.

'If an AAT member makes any disclosures which are likely to prejudice an investigation, following a report to the relevant person concerning money laundering, the member

	✓
has committed the criminal offence of tipping off.'	
should consult the AAT Ethics Advice Line.'	
may be liable to disciplinary action.'	

(b)   Rohinder is an AAT member on an assurance engagement at Poster plc. During the course of the engagement he has become aware of client staff disguising the nature and source of certain funds which Rohinder believes derive from tax evasion.

Complete the following sentence by selecting the appropriate option from the list below.

'Rohinder must report his suspicions so as to avoid a charge of ...

■   money laundering.'

■   failure to disclose.'

■   tipping off.'

Task 2.10

(a) Dominic, an AAT member, has been employed for some years by Hill plc. He feels that his immediate manager Serena poses a threat to his ability to perform his duties with the appropriate degree of professional competence and due care, as she has deliberately concealed evidence of criminal acts. Dominic has not been able to reduce this threat sufficiently with relevant safeguards. He therefore wishes to make a protected disclosure to the board of Hill plc.

Answer the following question by selecting the appropriate option.

What is Dominic's position as a whistle-blower in relation to the Public Interest Disclosure Act?

	✓
He will not be protected unless he discloses to a legal adviser.	
He will be protected provided he acts in good faith.	
He will not be protected as this is not a qualifying disclosure.	

(b) Answer the following question by selecting the appropriate option.

To which of the following disclosures does the Public Interest Disclosure Act extend?

	✓
Professional negligence	
Endangerment of an individual's health and safety	
Environmental damage	
Breach of contract	

(c) When reporting suspicion of money laundering, an AAT member in practice must make a 'required disclosure'.

Identify which items of information should be included in the disclosure by selecting the appropriate items from the list below.

	✓
Items of information	Relevant disclosure
The identity of the suspect (if known).	
The whereabouts of the suspect (if known).	
Information on which suspicion of money laundering is based.	
The nature of the laundered property (if known).	
The whereabouts of the laundered property (if known).	
The type of money laundering offence that has been committed.	

Professional ethics
Practice assessment 3

Section 1

Task 1.1

(a)   Complete the following sentence about the AAT fundamental principles by selecting the appropriate option from the list below.

'A member who is straightforward and honest in all professional and business relationships is following the fundamental principle of ...

■   Professional behaviour.'

■   Integrity.'

■   Objectivity.'

(b)   Decide whether the following sentence is true or false.

'The conceptual framework approach to ethics requires AAT members to comply with a prescribed set of ethical rules.'

| True/False |

Task 1.2

(a) Identify whether each of the following statements are true or false by selecting the appropriate option.

✓

	True	*False*
The AAT Code of Professional Ethics only applies to members who work in practice		
Failure to comply with the AAT Code of Professional Ethics is a criminal offence		

(b) When faced with an ethical issue the Institute of Business Ethics recommends applying a simple ethical test. From the list below select three elements of this test.

Select **three** options.

✓

Honesty	
Transparency	
Confidentiality	
Effect	
Fairness	
Legality	

Task 1.3

(a)   For each of the following professional bodies decide whether it is a sponsoring body of the AAT.

(Tick all that apply)

✓

	Sponsoring body
Chartered Institute of Management Accountants (CIMA)	
Institute of Chartered Accountants Scotland (ICAS)	
International Federation of Accountants (IFAC)	
Auditing Practices Board (APB)	
Institute of Chartered Accountants in England and Wales (ICAEW)	

(b)   Identify whether the following statement is true or false.

'The AAT is required by law to base its Code of Ethics on the International Federation of Accountants (IFAC) approved Code of Ethics for Professional Accountants.'

True/False

Task 1.4

Complete the following sentence by selecting the appropriate option from the list below.

'Organisations generally introduce their own business codes of ethics to...

- ■   provide their employees with a rigorous set of ethical rules to comply with.'
- ■   help their employees to make the right decision when faced with an ethical dilemma.'
- ■   identify the legal implications of all decisions that their employees make.'

Task 1.5

(a)   Oliver, an AAT member in practice, is preparing the year end payroll for his client, Shoona. Shoona has asked Oliver to pay the staff bonuses in cash so that neither the business nor the employees will have to pay National Insurance or Income Tax. She says that in return she will pay Oliver a cash bonus of £200.

In this situation Shoona could be prosecuted under which of the following legislation?

	✓
Fraud Act	
Health & Safety Act	
Bribery Act	

(b)   Complete the following sentence by inserting the correct number in the space provided.

'The Money Laundering Regulations 2007 apply to a member in practice when the member acts in relation to a transaction or series of related transactions amounting to .... euros or more.'

Task 1.6

(a)   Who of the following are required to complete the AAT's Continuing Professional Development (CPD) Cycle?

(Tick all that apply)   ✓

	Required to complete CPD Cycle
AAT student members	
AAT members in practice	
AAT members in business	
AAT fellow members	

(b)   An AAT member in practice must complete the AAT's CPD cycle at least how many times in a twelve month period?

Select **one** option.

	✓
Once	
Twice	
Three times	

Task 1.7

(a) Marcus is a member in practice. His sister Erin holds 40% of the shares in Ponypower Ltd. Erin has asked Marcus to carry out an assignment for Ponypower Ltd.

Complete the following sentence by selecting the appropriate option from the list below.

'Before accepting the assignment Marcus must ensure that he has adequate safeguards in place to minimise the threats to his compliance with the fundamental ethical principles of ....

- ■ Confidentiality and professional behaviour.'
- ■ Professional competence and due care and professional behaviour.'
- ■ Professional behaviour and objectivity.'
- ■ Integrity and confidentiality.'

(b) Enzo, an AAT member, is the senior accountant in an accountancy firm. The firm has recently employed two new trainees, Juliet, who is the granddaughter of one of the partners in the practice, and Seth. Enzo has noticed that Juliet regularly arrives back from lunch 15 minutes late. He has also become aware that Juliet is always given the more interesting work to do while Seth seems always to be making tea and coffee and doing the photocopying.

In order to behave in a fair manner in these circumstances what is the most appropriate action for Enzo to take?

Select **one** option from the list below.

	✓
Explain to Seth that he thinks the partner who is Juliet's grandfather is treating him unfairly	
Discuss the situation with Juliet's grandfather and explain that he does not feel Seth and Juliet are being treated equally	
Ensure that where possible he makes Juliet do the photocopying and tea and coffee making	
Give all the interesting roles on the assignments he manages to Seth	

(c) Gabriel is an AAT member in practice who works for Samuels & Strauss LLP. One of the partners, Andrew, has recently quoted for some work for a new client without asking Gabriel whether the quote is realistic. Gabriel believes that he and his staff will be unable to carry out the work to an acceptable standard for this fee.

Identify how this situation represents a threat to one of Gabriel's fundamental principles.

Select **one** option from the list below.

✓

This is a self-review threat to professional competence and due care	
This is a self-interest threat to professional competence and due care	
This is a self-review threat to professional behaviour	
This is a self-interest threat to professional behaviour	

(d) In the situation detailed above which of the following would be the most appropriate safeguard for Gabriel to put into place?

Select **one** option from the list below.

✓

Gabriel should refuse to carry out the assignment under any circumstances	
Gabriel should resign from Samuels & Strauss LLP	
Gabriel should discuss the fee that has been quoted with Andrew and explain that he and his staff will need more time to complete the work	
Gabriel should carry out the assignment to the best of his ability in the time allocated to it	

Task 1.8

(a) Arthur is an AAT member employed by Redwell plc, an insurance company. The board of directors have recently announced that they are planning to make 12% of the firm's workforce redundant.

Complete the following sentence by identifying the most appropriate option.

'The circumstances at Redwell plc indicate that Arthur may face.......

- an advocacy threat to his fundamental principles.'
- a familiarity threat to his fundamental principles.'
- a self-review threat to his fundamental principles.'
- a self-interest threat to his fundamental principles.'

(b)   Charlene is a member in practice. Her client, Remarkable Wines Ltd is a wholesale wine merchant which is about to celebrate its 25th anniversary of being in business.

The Managing Director of Remarkable Wines Ltd presents Charlene with six bottles of champagne, one for each member of her team.

What must Charlene do before she can accept the gift of the champagne?

✓

She must tell him that she can only accept one bottle of champagne	
She must check to ensure that each bottle of champagne costs less than £20	
She must ensure that all other suppliers to Remarkable Wines are being offered the same gift	
She cannot accept the champagne under any circumstances	

(c)   Complete the following sentence by selecting the appropriate option from the list below.

'A member in practice must be independent on..........

■   all assignments.'
■   assurance assignments only.'

(d)   Darren is an AAT member in practice who is currently working on an assignment for Rollington Ltd. The Finance Director of Rollington Ltd has asked if Darren can reduce the fee for the assignment by 20%. The Finance Director says that he is in negotiations with another accounting practice and will consider changing accountants if Darren does not reduce the fee.

Complete the following sentence by selecting the appropriate option from the list below.

'In this situation Darren faces.....

■   an advocacy threat to his objectivity.'
■   a familiarity threat to his integrity.'
■   an intimidation threat to his objectivity.'

Section 2

Task 2.1

(a)   Decide whether each of the following statements is true or false.

(i)   'The AAT Disciplinary Regulations are legally enforceable by the AAT.'

| True/False |

(ii)   'Where there is conclusive proof of misconduct by an AAT member, the member will automatically have his/her membership suspended.'

| True/False |

(b)   Mischa is an AAT member who owns her own accounting practice employing a team of eight staff. She is not aware of the requirements of the Data Protection Act and consequently has failed to notify the Information Commissioner of the way in which her business processes data.

What are the consequences of this for Mischa?

Select **one** option from the list below.

	✓
There is no issue as Mischa only employs eight members of staff	
Mischa has committed a criminal offence under the Data Protection Act and could be fined if convicted	
There is no issue unless she fails to respond to a formal request from the Information Commissioner	

Task 2.2

(a)   It is 7 March and Jonathan, an AAT member in practice, has been asked by one of his clients to hold on to £6,000 until the end of the tax year (5 April).

What is the best course of action for Jonathan to take in these circumstances?

Select **one** option from the list below.

✓

Jonathan should not hold the money for his client because it exceeds the permitted limit for a member to hold client money	
Jonathan can hold the client money because the time period is less than one month	
Jonathan should identify where the money has come from and then hold the £6,000 separately from his own accounts	
Jonathan should identify where the money has come from and then deposit it in his business account until the end of the tax year	

(b)   It is an offence for an accountant to fail to disclose a suspicion or knowledge of money laundering.

Complete the following sentence by selecting an option from the list below.

'The maximum penalty for failure to disclose is .... imprisonment or an unlimited fine.'

■   12 months

■   5 years

■   7 years

■   17 years

Task 2.3

(a)   Jimmy is an AAT member in business who works for Direll plc. His manager is currently interviewing for a new finance assistant. While passing his manager's office Jimmy sees Cassandra leaving after an interview. Before joining Direll plc Jimmy worked in practice with Cassandra. During this time Cassandra was formally disciplined by the AAT.

In the circumstances, ethically, what action should Jimmy take?

Select **one** option.   ✓

This is confidential information which he should not share with his manager	
This is confidential information so he should tell his manager 'off the record' and ask him not to tell anyone how he found out	
Details of disciplinary proceedings are published by the AAT, therefore this is not confidential information so Jimmy should tell his manager of his concerns	

(b)   Which of the following statements best describes an AAT member's duty of confidentiality to his/her client?

Select **one** option.   ✓

An AAT member has a duty of confidentiality to the client for the duration of the assignment only	
An AAT member has an on-going duty of confidentiality to the client both during and after the completion of the assignment	

Task 2.4

(a)   In which of the following circumstances is it not permitted for an AAT member to disclose confidential information?

Select **one** option from the list below.

✓

Where disclosure is required by law but not authorised by the client	
To respond to an investigation by the AAT	
Where confidential documents are required as evidence in a court of law	
Where disclosure is permitted by law but not authorised by the client	

(b)   Omar, an AAT member in practice, has a suspicion that his client, Jonathan, has been involved in money laundering. In these circumstances which of the following is true regarding client confidentiality?

✓

Omar cannot report his suspicions while he is working for Jonathan as this would be a breach of client confidentiality	
Omar must tell Jonathan of his suspicions to ensure that he does not breach client confidentiality	
Omar should report his suspicions as this will be a protected disclosure so Omar will be protected against allegations of breach of confidentiality	

Task 2.5

(a) Alicia is an AAT member working in business. Her manager has asked her to complete the company's VAT return for the previous quarter. During this quarter the business has completed some complex asset purchases and disposals. Alicia has never completed a VAT return before.

What is the best course of action for Alicia in these circumstances?

Select **one** option from the list below.

✓

Immediately contact the AAT Ethics Advice Line	
Alicia should explain her inexperience and ask for appropriate support and expertise while completing the VAT return	
Alicia should refuse to complete the VAT return	
Alicia should complete the VAT return and hope that there is sufficient guidance on the HMRC website	

(b) Reggie has recently been offered a job at Icarus Ltd. In his application form Reggie said that he has experience in accounting for leases; in fact he has only worked on one leasing transaction at his previous employment and he was supervised throughout by his manager. His new manager has allocated him sole responsibility for lease accounting.

If Reggie accepts this responsibility which of his fundamental principles will be compromised most?

Select **one** option from the list below.

✓

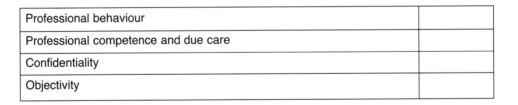

Professional behaviour	
Professional competence and due care	
Confidentiality	
Objectivity	

Task 2.6

(a) Complete the following sentence about ownership of documents.

'Kevin is acting as an agent for his client, Wilbur. Under UK law documents generated as part of the assignment will be the property of ....'

(b) Under the Money Laundering Regulations copies of the evidence an accountant has used for customer due diligence must be kept for how long?

Select **one** option from the list below.

	✓
5 years from the date on which the accountant's relationship with the client starts	
5 years from the date on which the accountant's relationship with the client ends	
3 years from the date on which the accountant's relationship with the client starts	
3 years from the date on which the accountant's relationship with the client ends	

Task 2.7

(a)   Edmund is an AAT member working in a small accounting practice with three staff. He is working at one of his client's premises when he finds documents that raise his suspicions of money laundering.

In these circumstances what should Edmund do?

Select the appropriate option from the list below.

✓

Tell the client immediately of his suspicions and explain that if she is money laundering his firm can no longer work for her	
Report his suspicions to the Serious Organised Crime Agency	
Report his suspicions to the police	

(b)   Consider the following sentence and decide whether it is true or false.

'Failure to include income in a tax return constitutes money laundering.'

True/False

Task 2.8

'Where a person knows or suspects that a money laundering investigation is being conducted or is about to be conducted and falsifies, conceals or destroys documents relevant to the investigation, or causes that to happen.'

Which of the following is the sentence above a description of?

✓

Tipping off	
Failure to disclose	
Prejudicing an investigation	
Money Laundering	

Task 2.9

Geraldine is an AAT member who works for a large accounting practice. Whilst preparing the tax return for her client, Johnny, she finds evidence of Johnny purchasing stolen property.

(a) In these circumstances who should Geraldine report her suspicions to?

Select **one** option.

	✓
Johnny	
AAT	
Money Laundering Reporting Officer	
Serious Organised Crime Agency	

(b) Geraldine must make her disclosure in which type of report?

Select **one** option.

	✓
A suspicious activity report (SAR)	
An internal report	
An audit report	

Task 2.10

Arlene is an AAT member who works in business for Bradfield Ltd. She has 'blown the whistle' on some activities of her employer. She has made a protected disclosure under the Public Interest Disclosure Act (PIDA).

Decide whether the following statement is true or false.

'Bradfield Ltd is permitted to dismiss Arlene as a consequence of this protected disclosure.'

True/False

Practice assessment answers

1 Practice assessment – answers

Section 1

Task 1.1

(a) 'A member must not let his/her own bias or pressure from others affect decisions that the members makes. This is following the fundamental principle of **objectivity**.'

(b) 'The conceptual framework approach requires members to take ethical decisions that **comply with the fundamental ethical principles.**'

Task 1.2

(a) Mastering of particular skills and techniques acquired through learning and education and maintained through continuing professional development.

(b) Overseeing the regulatory activities of all the professional accounting bodies.

(c) True

Task 1.3

Is a member of CCAB	Is not a member of CCAB
ICAEW	IFAC
ICAS	FRC
ACCA	AAT
CIPFA	CIMA
ICAI	

Task 1.4

(a) False

(b) It is **advisable** for a business to introduce an ethical code, but it is not a **legal requirement.**

Task 1.5

(a) According to the Basel Committee on Banking Supervision, the definition of **operational** risk is the risk of loss resulting from inadequate or failed internal **processes**, people and systems or from external events.

(b) Verify the client's identity on the basis of documents, data or other reliable information.

Task 1.6

(a)

(b)   True

Task 1.7

(a)   Explain to Alice that it would be unethical to agree to her offer as they would both be breaching the fundamental principles of integrity and confidentiality

(b)   'This accusation is most likely to arise if Freddie says in his marketing material that he is a more ethical accountant than any other accountancy firm in the area.'

(c)   MAAT

(d)   'In exercising **professional judgement** a member should consider what a **reasonable** and informed third party having knowledge of all relevant information, including the significance of the threat and the safeguards applied, would conclude to be **unacceptable**.

Task 1.8

(a)   'For Verity this situation threatens both the fundamental principles of **objectivity and confidentiality.**'

(b)   Advise Rosie of relevant threats and safeguards that will protect Jim should her employer enter into any future contracts with Rosie's organisation.

(c)   'The requirement for an AAT member in practice to be independent of a client applies in relation to assurance clients only.'

(d)   'This situation presents a **self-interest threat** and the best course of action would be **to remove Harjit from the assurance engagement.**'

(e)   'This situation presents a **self-review** threat.'

      A policy preventing Roger from working as part of the assurance team for Weaver plc.

Section 2

Task 2.1

(a)   Nolan Principles: Selflessness, Openness

(b)   'AAT Disciplinary action will be taken against Miles if his conduct reflects adversely on the reputation of the AAT.'

Task 2.2

  (a) Agree to hold the money and open a client account for Roland that is separate from his business account

  (b) 'Where a person fails to disclose **any** information to a third party which he/she has a **legal** duty to disclose.'

Task 2.3

  (a)

	True	False
Andrea should not disclose this information to any other member of staff at Shine LLP.		✓
Andrea should not discuss this information with other members of staff at Glimmer Ltd.	✓	
Andrea should not use this information to the advantage of Shine LLP	✓	
Andrea should not discuss this information with her husband.	✓	

  (b) False

Task 2.4

Where the information is required as evidence in a court of law.	✓
When authorised by a client or employer.	✓
Where the law has been broken and the information has to be disclosed to the relevant authorities.	✓
When the professional relationship between the client and the member has been terminated.	

Task 2.5

  (a) False

  (b) 'Henrico may nonetheless undertake the project if he has adequate support.'

Task 2.6

(a)　'If a client asks for a document to be produced by an AAT member as part of an assignment then the document will belong to **the client.**'

(b)　'The Limitation Act 1980 states that the time limit for legal actions under simple contract law is **six** years.'

Task 2.7

(a)　'Ellery is obliged to report the client's refusal and the facts surrounding it to the Serious Organised Crime Agency (SOCA).'

(b)　There is no lower limit

Task 2.8

'Royston is being offered **an inducement** which will threaten is adherence to the fundamental principles. His immediate response should be to **obtain advice from the AAT.**'

Task 2.9

(a)　If Amir does not report his concerns he may be charged with **failure to disclose.**'

(b)　However his concerns should not be raised with the client or he may be guilty of **tipping off.**'

Task 2.10

(a)　The Whistleblowers Charter

(b)　Breach of contract

Professional negligence

(c)　'Accounting practices should have training and procedures in place to ensure that they comply with the reporting requiring for money laundering. If procedures are not in place they may be liable for **a fine and/or imprisonment.**'

2 Practice assessment – answers

Section 1

Task 1.1

(a) Integrity.

(b) Identify, evaluate and respond to threats to compliance with the fundamental principles.

Task 1.2

(a) Acknowledgement of duties to society as a whole in addition to duties to the employer or client.

(b) The Professional Oversight Board (POB)

(c) make the right choice between alternative courses of action.

Task 1.3

Sponsoring body of the AAT	Not a sponsoring body of the AAT
▣ ICAEW	▣ ICAI
▣ ICAS	▣ ACCA
▣ CIMA	▣ IFAC
▣ CIPFA	▣ FRC

Task 1.4

(a) False.

(b) To ensure that there is consistency of conduct by employees across the organisation.

Task 1.5

(a) processes, people and systems.'

(b) Verify the client's identity on the basis of documents, data or other reliable information.

Task 1.6

(a) professional competence and due care.

(b) True.

Task 1.7

(a)   Because she lacks integrity, inform her that she will not be offered the job.

(b)   makes a disparaging reference in an advertisement to the work of Iqbal, an ACCA member.'

(c)   Prohibited element: MAAT

(d)   'In exercising professional judgement, a member should consider what a reasonable and informed third party, having knowledge of all relevant information, including the significance of the threat and the safeguards applied, would conclude to be unacceptable.'

Task 1.8

(a)   objectivity and confidentiality.

(b)   Advise Oonagh of relevant threats and safeguards that will protect Niall should he receive such an offer from Oonagh's organization.

(c)   assurance clients only.

(d)   self-interest threat; to remove Quentin from the assurance engagement.

(e)   self-interest.

A policy requiring Helena to notify the firm of such an offer.

A policy requiring Helena's removal from the assurance engagement with Bowen plc.

Section 2

Task 2.1

(a)   Nolan Principles: Accountability, Honesty

(b)   if his conduct reflects adversely on the reputation of the AAT.'

Task 2.2

(a)   Hold the money separately from his own money and that of his business.

(b)   Fraud by abuse of position.

Task 2.3

(a)   using the information to the advantage of Sueka LLP.

(b)   True

Task 2.4

(a)   Where there is a professional duty to disclose in the public interest, and this is not prohibited by law.

(b)   the Serious Organised Crime Agency.

Task 2.5

(a)   breach of contract and professional negligence.

(b)   has adequate support.

Task 2.6

(a)   Pippa Ltd's.'

(b)   *Right of lien exists*

The documents belong to the client.

The documents are in the member's possession by proper means.

Work has been done by the member on the documents for which the fee is outstanding.

Task 2.7

(a)   the Money Laundering Reporting Officer (MLRO).'

(b)   False

(c)   14

Task 2.8

an intimidation threat; obtaining advice from the AAT.'

Task 2.9

(a)   has committed the criminal offence of tipping off.'

(b)   failure to disclose.'

Task 2.10

(a)   He will be protected provided he acts in good faith.

(b)   Endangerment of an individual's health and safety.

Environmental damage.

(c)   *Relevant disclosure:*

The identity of the suspect (if known).

Information on which suspicion of money laundering is based.

The whereabouts of the laundered property (if known).

3 Practice assessment – answers

Section 1

Task 1.1

(a) Integrity

(b) False - the conceptual framework provides guidance for an AAT member in any ethical dilemma that he/she may face

Task 1.2

(a)

	True	False
The AAT Code of Professional Ethics only applies to members who work in practice		✓
Failure to comply with the AAT Code of Professional Ethics is a criminal offence		✓

(b) **Transparency**, **Effect**, and **Fairness**

Task 1.3

(a)

	Sponsoring body
Chartered Institute of Management Accountants (CIMA)	✓
Institute of Chartered Accountants Scotland (ICAS)	✓
International Federation of Accountants (IFAC)	
Auditing Practices Board (APB)	
Institute of Chartered Accountants in England and Wales (ICAEW)	✓

(b) False - the AAT Code of Ethics is not legally binding

Task 1.4

'Organisations generally introduce their own business codes of ethics to **help their employees to make the right decision when faced with an ethical dilemma**.'

Task 1.5

(a) Bribery Act

(b) 15,000

Task 1.6

(a)

	Required to complete CPD Cycle
AAT student members	
AAT members in practice	✓
AAT members in business	
AAT fellow members*	✓

* a fellow member is a member who has belonged to the AAT for more than 5 years

(b) Twice

Task 1.7

(a) 'Before accepting the assignment Marcus must ensure that he has adequate safeguards in place to minimise the threats to his compliance with the fundamental ethical principles of **Professional behaviour and objectivity**.'

(b) Discuss the situation with Juliet's grandfather and explain that he does not feel Seth and Juliet are being treated equally

(c) This is a self-interest threat to professional competence and due care

(d) Gabriel should discuss the fee that has been quoted with Andrew and explain that he and his staff will need more time to complete the work

Task 1.8

(a) 'The circumstances at Redwell plc indicate that Arthur may face **a self-interest threat to his fundamental principles**.'

(b) She must ensure that all other suppliers to Remarkable Wines are being offered the same gift

(c) 'A member in practice must be independent on **assurance assignments only**.'

(d) 'In this situation Darren faces **an intimidation threat to his objectivity**.'

Section 2

Task 2.1

(a)

(i) False

(ii) False

(b) Mischa has committed a criminal offence under the Data Protection Act and could be fined if convicted

Task 2.2

    (a)   Jonathan should identify where the money has come from and then hold the £6,000 separately from his own accounts

    (b)   'The maximum penalty for failure to disclose is **5 years** imprisonment or an unlimited fine.'

Task 2.3

    (a)   Details of disciplinary proceedings are published by the AAT, therefore this is not confidential information so Jimmy should tell his manager of his concerns

    (b)   An AAT member has an on-going duty of confidentiality to the client both during and after the completion of the assignment

Task 2.4

    (a)   Where disclosure is permitted by law but not authorised by the client

    (b)   Omar should report his suspicions as this will be a protected disclosure so Omar will be protected against allegations of breach of confidentiality

Task 2.5

    (a)   Alicia should explain her inexperience and ask for appropriate support and expertise while completing the VAT return

    (b)   Professional competence and due care

Task 2.6

    (a)   'Kevin is acting as an agent for his client, Wilbur. Under UK law documents generated as part of the assignment will be the property of **Wilbur**.'

    (b)   5 years from the date on which the accountant's relationship with the client ends

Task 2.7

    (a)   Report his suspicions to the Serious Organised Crime Agency

    (b)   True

Task 2.8

    Prejudicing an investigation

Task 2.9

    (a)   Money Laundering Reporting Officer

    (b)   An internal report

Task 2.10

    True - Bradfield Ltd can dismiss Arlene, however she is protected, and can claim for unfair dismissal

for your notes